Precious and the Good Shepherd
A Rejected Lamb's Story of Love

Written by Ray Carman
Illustrated by David Olson
Edited by Deborah Secor

Other titles available from Ray Carman

Enjoy the Shepherd: Daily Lessons From Sheep
A daily devotional aimed at leading the reader back to the feet of Jesus, our Good Shepherd

God's Agents of Smash
The story of a loving God who would do anything to remove the barriers between Him and His people

You can find both of these titles at:
EnjoyTheShepherd.com/shop

Please visit our Youtube channel: Enjoy The Shepherd
Join our Facebook page: Facebook.com/EnjoyTheShepherd
Follow on Instagram: instagram.com/EnjoyTheShepherd

ISBN 978-0-9984858-2-9

Gratitude from author Ray Carman...

I would like to thank my Good Shepherd, Jesus Christ, for finding me and rescuing me in His love. This story is based on the true story of a lamb named Precious born on our farm, but her life is but a mirror of what God has done in my life through his son Jesus! Without Jesus, I truly would be lost.

I would also like to thank my wife, Katie, for her deep commitment to God and to loving me, especially through these past couple of years. Running a business and working on writing and farming can often cause interesting issues, but your love and support through this time has been invaluable.

Lastly, I want to thank my children, Hailey, Raygan, Truett, and Knox for all your help on the farm in raising our sheep. Dad loves each one of you and I look forward to the day you will lead your own "lambs" to the feet of the Good Shepherd!

Thanks to all who had a hand in making this book a reality. Lisa Tesch, thanks for your kind words and support in the writing process. Deborah, your editing skills are truly appreciated by all who will read this. David Olson, I cannot say enough about your hard work and illustrations as they made this story come to life. Angela Free, I know you put in countless hours putting the pages together and formatting the book, so thank you very much.

To the reader, thanks for picking up this story and reading it. I hope and pray you will see the love of Jesus for you and therefore be like Precious, and lead others back to his feet. Mostly, my hearts desire is that you, dear reader and listener, will Go Enjoy The Shepherd!

Gratitude from illustrator David Olson...

I want to thank the Lord for the opportunity to use the talents He has given me. It was a blessing to work with Ray, illustrating Precious and the Good Shepherd. It is a wonderful story that I prayerfully hope will touch the hearts of many young readers, and even adults. It gives us a picture of God's wonderful love and faithfulness, and when we witness that love in our own lives we want to tell others about the Good Shepherd. Psalm 23

Out in the field stood a lovely Sheep whose name was Precious. All around her there stood luscious green grass next to a calm stream. Playing close by were her two grandchildren, Liam and Lily, the newest lambs on the farm.

Liam and Lilly were so full of energy. They loved to run, bounce, hop and play. Precious enjoyed watching them frolic around in the field. Life was full of joy and she looked forward to each day seeing the One she loved the most, The Good Shepherd....

Liam and Lilly had heard the story before, but they wanted to hear it once more! "Please Granny Please, tell us again about the Good Shepherd and how He loved you so much!"

Precious never tired of talking of the Good Shepherd and his love, so she laid down in the shade to tell her story! Liam, Lily and all their friends gathered around as she began.

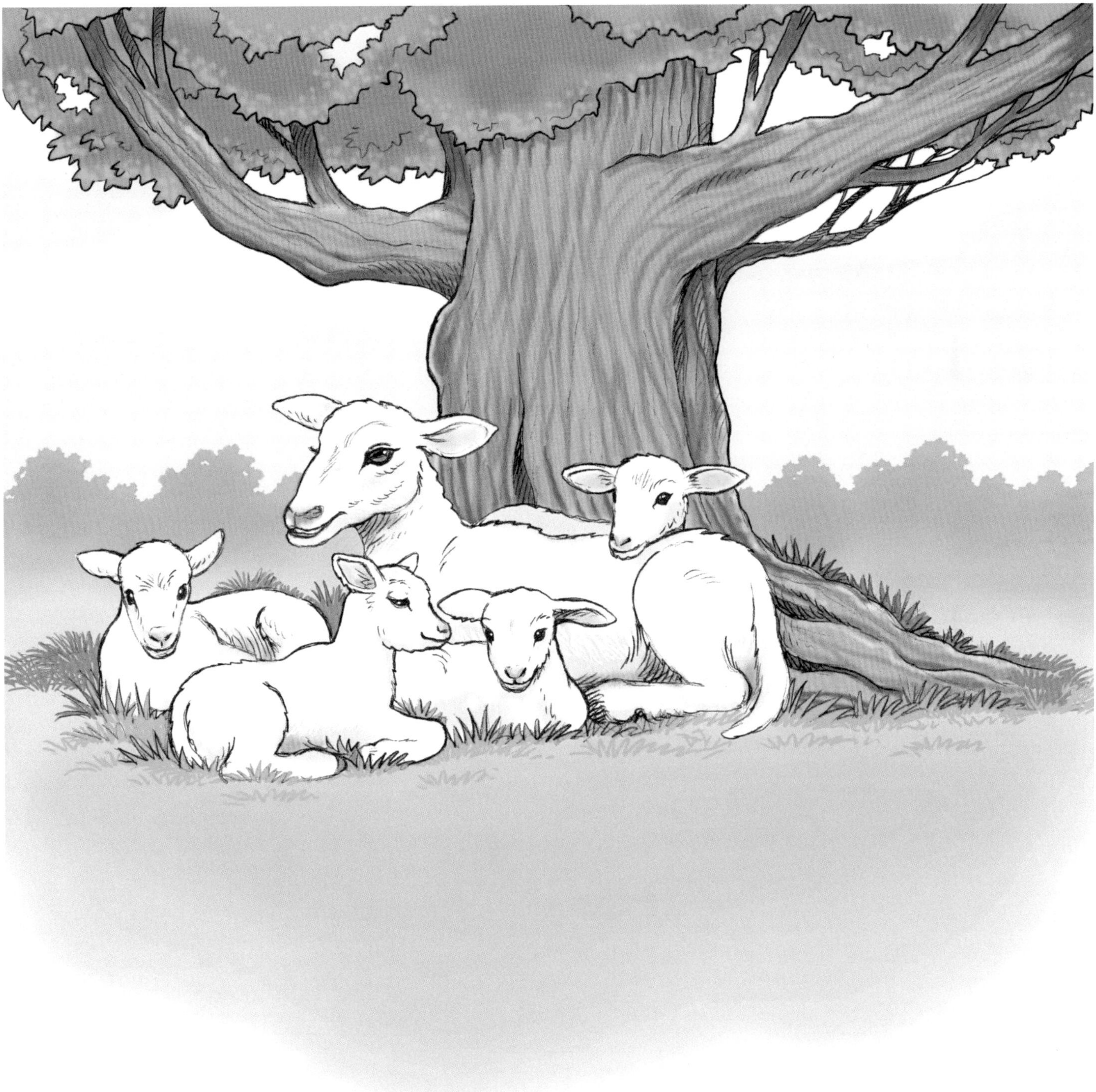

"As you all know, my life has not always been so wonderful. When I was born, something happened and my mother and I got separated! Something made her run away and I was left all alone.

I walked around looking for her, and asking all the other sheep where she had gone. I cried and I cried, but it seemed like no one was listening.

Suddenly, I saw this man walking up to me. I was dirty, nasty, and REALLY hungry. He picked me up gently and asked me, "Where is your mom little one?"

He carried me in his arms and brought me to a beautiful sheep who had another lamb, It was my Mom! I was so excited to see her and to be with her again! I immediately went up to her to get some milk, but she did not seem excited to see me! She refused to let me drink. I wondered what was wrong.

The man who had put me with my mom stood close by and watched us. I could tell by the look on his face, he was concerned. It was almost like he knew how I was feeling! I tried my best to get milk again from my mom, but she would not let me drink and she started to walk away with my brother.

Suddenly, I found myself in the arms of this big man again and He whispered, "It is going to be alright little one, everything will be okay." He carried me and my brother to a stall in his barn. My mom followed him into the stall....

"Yay!" I thought. "Now mom will clean me off and let me have the milk I need so bad. I just know she is going to love me!" But that is not what happened. In fact, things got worse. Mom kept feeding my brother, but she refused to love me. I was so confused!

Every time I asked her for milk, she said no and would push me away by butting me with her head. Why was my own mother pushing me away? All I could do was cry!

As I walked around the stall, I kept seeing this man standing there. He was watching me with great love in his eyes. He even tried to help my mom understand that I was hers and that it was okay to feed me and take care of me. But my mom would not listen to him, and she started to hurt me because she was hitting me so hard! She had rejected me!!!!

Why? Why had mom decided to not love me? Why did she decide to not take care of me? I wondered if there was something wrong with me! Was there something I had done to make her not want me? Was I not pretty enough? Why was I not good enough? All I could do was wonder why she had rejected me!

After several hours of trying his best to get me some of mom's milk, the big man picked me back up and whispered softly, "It's okay little girl, your mom does not want you, but I will carry you home and I will raise you myself." Then he told me his name, "I am the Good Shepherd, now what shall I name you?"

I was confused and was not sure what to do. I so wanted to be with my mom and brother, but she did not want me. As he carried me, I was afraid and several times I tried to get away from him. But his strong arms gently tucked me in and he kept telling me, "It's okay little one, I will take care of you!" One look in his eyes and I could tell he really loved me!

He took me in his house and introduced me to his kids! This was the first time I heard him say my name! His gentle, but strong voice said, "Hey kids, meet Precious!"

The next few days were a blur. I was so little and so hungry, but the Good Shepherd was always there to feed me! He fixed me a bed in his home and kept me warm! There were times I could tell he was really tired because of all the work he had to do making sure I was okay, but he never complained and always said, "Hi Precious, you are such a good lamb! I love you very much!"

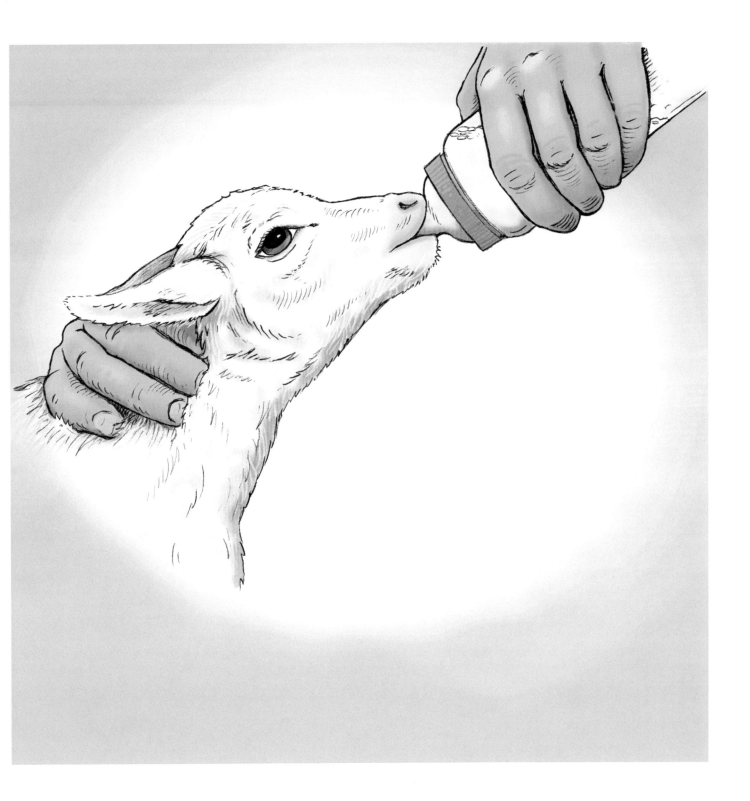

This was so hard for me to understand! How could he love me if my own mother did not want me? There were times I would think of how much I missed her, and it would make me cry out loud! Whenever I cried, the Good Shepherd would come in and hold me close and gently whisper, "It's okay Precious, I love you and everything will be okay!"

Because of his constant love, I started to believe I would be alright. He would take me out in his yard and let me run and play! Whenever I made a mess in his home, he would clean it up and tell me he did not mind! He always showed me love, and he made me feel special! I looked forward to spending time with him and being by his side!

He would let me sleep in his arms when I was tired. He let me run and play and go with him on his walks. As we walked he told me stories of how he was rejected when he was little too. He told me he understood how much I was hurting, but he reassured me everything would be okay! I could not believe a man as nice as him had been hurt like me, but the tear in his eye told me it was true. Somehow though, the pain he had felt had only made him love those who hurt him even more! I hoped one day I could be like him!!!

I eventually went back to the farm with him and it was there that I saw her again! My mom walked by and my brother was with her, but she did not even recognize me. For a moment I was sad again, until I heard his voice calling, "Come on Precious, let's go home!" I wagged my tail and ran to be with him again!

On that day, the Good Shepherd began to tell me about how one day I would go back to the farm and be his biggest helper. He said, "Precious, very soon you will go back to the farm and I will need you to tell the others of my love. Some of them, like your mom, do not realize how much I love them. I will need you to tell them about my love and lead them back to me!

"Precious, I wish you could have known the love of your mother and brother, but I am so glad I got to show you my love. I know it was hard on you, but loving you has brought me great joy and happiness! Thank you for allowing me to love you.

"When you go back, it will be hard again, because I cannot stay there with you all the time. I have other lambs, like you, who I need to show my love to. But, I will never forsake you or forget about you. I will come every day and walk in the fields and call your name. When you hear my voice, come running to me! When you do, all my other sheep, including your mom and brother, will follow you! Then I will be able to show them how much I love and care for them! Can you do that for me, Precious?"

I could not speak the words that he used, but I could jump around to let him know I would. I was excited that he was going to let me tell the other sheep and lambs about his amazing love! I looked in his eyes, hoping he could understand how much I appreciated him for showing me his love.

When the day arrived for me to return to the farm, I could tell that the Good Shepherd was both happy and sad. He loved me so much and he really wanted to hold me close forever. But he loved his other sheep very much, and he needed someone to go tell them how much He loved them! I was sad too, but excited at the same time that he had chosen me to be the one who could go tell the others of His great love!

He carried me one last time, back to the same place he had found me and put me in the middle of all his other sheep. He hugged me close and whispered in my ear, "I love you Precious, now go and tell them! I will be back everyday to check on you and make sure you are okay!"

With that, The Good Shepherd closed the gate and I watched him walk away. I cried a little, and when he turned, I could see a tear in his eye too! He waved one last time and disappeared over the hill. I turned around and saw my mom, my brother, and all the other sheep. I really wanted to be back with the Shepherd, living in his house, but I knew he had given me a very important job to do. He wanted me to tell all of these other sheep, including my own family, about his love for them. I glanced back one last time to see if maybe he was coming back. I desperately wanted to have him hold me again, but I knew I had a job to do. It was not going to be easy, because I was just a little lamb, but I loved the Good Shepherd so much, I just had to try.

By this time, all the lambs and big sheep had gathered under the shade of the big oak tree to hear the story of the Good Shepherd again! They had come to enjoy hearing the story of the Shepherd's love for them! As Precious finished up her story, a voice called out from over the hill! "Precious!!!! I am here!"

"It's the Good Shepherd," Liam shouted to Lilly! They all looked up to find Precious running as fast as she could. The Good Shepherd had kept his promise and visited her every day, and she looked forward to her time to be by his side! All the lambs and other sheep ran after her, trying to beat her to the Good Shepherd, but even in her old age, Precious was always the first one to his side!

Precious stood at his feet and he gently bent down and patted her head, "Well done girl," He said, "you have led all the sheep back to me again!" Precious looked back at the lambs and sheep crowding around the Good Shepherd, each enjoying his love. The same love she had first experienced as a rejected lamb! In her heart, Precious was overwhelmed again by His love as she stood at the feet of the Good Shepherd. She realized how important her life and story had been and how many sheep she had been allowed to lead back to the Good Shepherd's feet. Though her life had begun as a rejected lamb, the love He had shown her had washed all that pain away.

Until it was time for her to return to the paradise of His backyard, she knew she must continue telling her story to other sheep she met along the way. She never stopped telling the story of how she met the Good Shepherd, about how He had loved her, a rejected lamb that He now called "Precious!"

Made in the USA
Lexington, KY
17 February 2018